A Year with Friends

A Year with Friends

by John Seven   illustrated by Jana Christy

SCHOLASTIC INC.

ISBN 978-0-545-83698-2

12 11 10 9 8 7 6 5 4 3 2 1   15 16 17 18 19 20/0

Printed in the U.S.A.   40

First Scholastic printing, January 2015

Book design by Meagan Bennett

For our sons Harry and Hugo,
who make every year a new adventure

January

is time for rolling down hills.

February

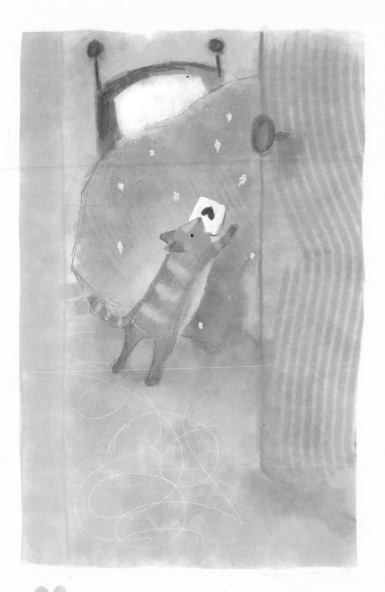

is time for snuggling.

March

is time to hold on to your hat.

April

is time to get messy.

May

is time for flowers.

June

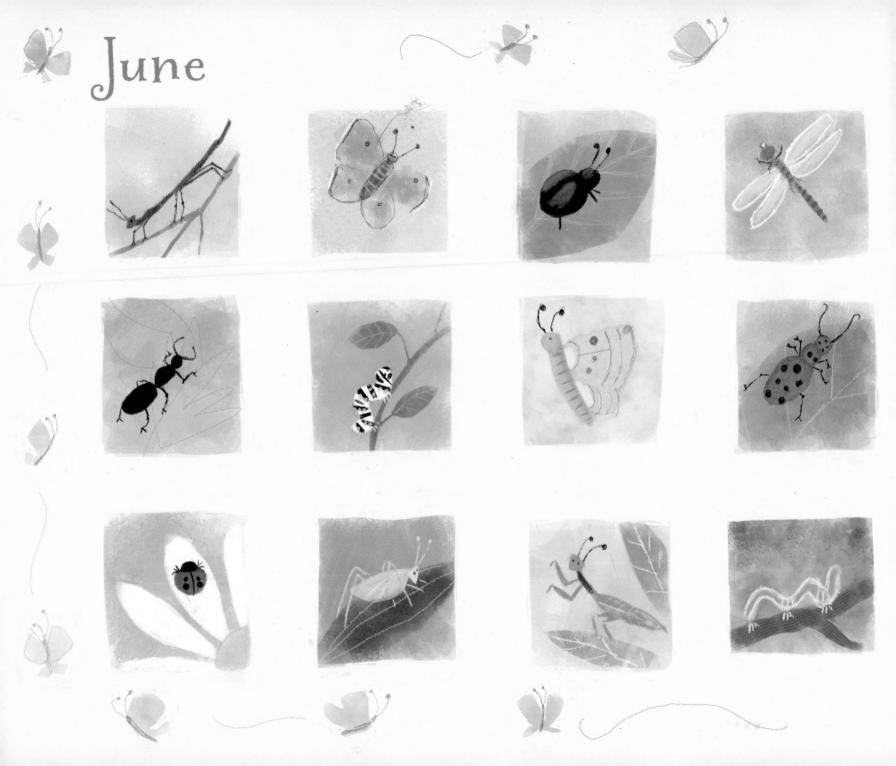

is time for bugs.

July

is time for fireworks.

August

is time for the beach.

September

is time for picking apples.

October

 is time for tricks and treats.

November

is time to feast together.

December

is time for sharing.

A new year

is time for fun with new friends!

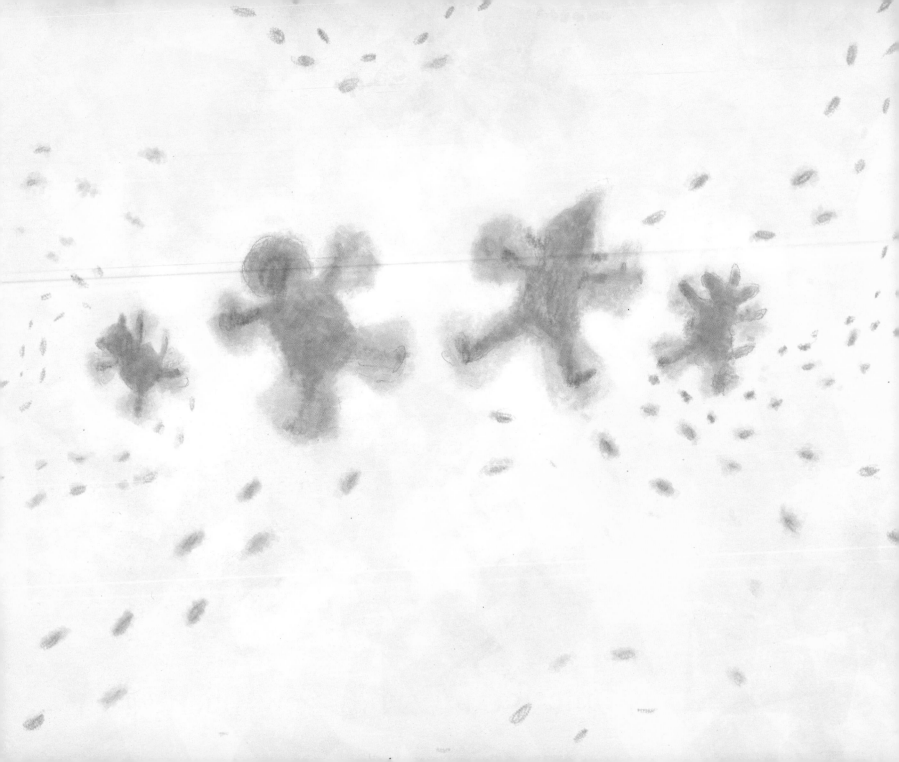